THIS POWER RANGERS JUNGLE FURY ANNUAL BELONGS TO:

NAME...

AGE...

FAVOURITE JUNGLE FURY RANGER:

....

POWER RANGERS JUNGLE FURY
ANNUAL 2010

www.jetix.co.uk

Power Rangers: TM & © 2009
BVS Entertainment, Inc. and
BVS International N.V.

EGMONT
We bring stories to life

First Published in Great Britain in 2009 by Egmont UK Limited,
239 Kensington High Street, London W8 6SA
ISBN 978 1 4052 4648 4
10 9 8 7 6 5 4 3 2 1
Printed in Italy
Editor: Kate Durrant Designer: Colin Treanor

CONTENTS

CALLING ALL RANGERS!

Welcome to your wild and wonderful Jungle Fury
Annual! Call to your Beast Spirit and help the latest team
of Power Rangers on their mission: to save the world
from evil Dai Shi and his army of animal spirits!

Turn the page for action-packed comic stories, top
Ranger profiles and super-fun puzzles. Well, what are
you waiting for – start the adventure now!

FRAN'S DIARY: THE JUNGLE FURY STORY

Fran is a friend to the Rangers and works at the Jungle Karma Pizza parlour. She has kept a diary about her experiences. Here are some of her entries . . .

Dear Diary,

I can't believe it. I'm working at Jungle Karma Pizza - my favourite restaurant in the whole world! I love pizza: cheese and tomato, pepperoni, Thriller Gorilla - that's a speciality of RJ's (he trains the Rangers and runs the pizza parlour). He makes up the funniest pizzas - like one time he tried to make Mount Kilimanjaro - he's crazy!

I was going into the pizza parlour almost every day - not that I didn't have anything else to do - I did. It's just that I, well . . . OK, I was getting kind of bored. My parents were really busy and my friends were all made up people in books . . . breathe. Sometimes RJ tells me to remember to breathe. I forget when I get too excited about something - you know, like pizza.

I have to say, I did think something odd was going on with my new friends. They kept going off on these oh-so-highly important and secretive missions. Then I found out - Lily, Theo and Casey are Power Rangers! Not only that but they're our only hope against this ancient evil guy, Dai Shi. Totally awesome!

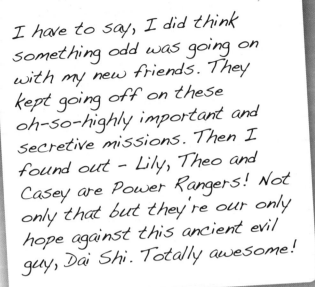

So it turns out Lily, Theo and Casey have these amazing martial arts skills and are using the upstairs of the restaurant as a training room. It's really cool up there. They've got a jukebox, all kinds of training equipment and these TVs which show what Dai Shi and his friends are up to. When the Rangers have to leave in a hurry, they swing on vines through a hole in the wall!

But I'll start at the beginning. The Rangers were studying at the super-elite Pai Zhuq martial arts academy. One of the teachers, Master Mao, was looking for three tough teens who could work as a team and be prepared to fight some of the nastiest baddies on earth. Their mission: to guard over the evil spirit, Dai Shi, who had been trapped in a chest for over 10,000 years! Master Mao decided on Casey, Theo and Lily. He chose Casey over a student called Jarrod, which made Jarrod kind of mad.

When Master Mao showed Lily, Casey and Theo the room where Dai Shi was kept, Jarrod burst in. He caused a fight and let Dai Shi escape from the chest! The evil spirit destroyed Master Mao and took on Jarrod's body. As he lay dying, Master Mao told the Rangers they had to go to Jungle Karma in Ocean Bluff to find their new master.

So, the three teens headed to Ocean Bluff. I'll just tell you a little about them. Casey's the least experienced member of the team, and sometimes he feels like he has to train twice as hard as the others. Even so, RJ thinks he has what it takes to lead the team. Theo's a total perfectionist and has to do everything just right - especially fighting! Theo really likes Lily - and I like teasing him about that! Lily's really cool. She was a cheerleader in high school and now she uses her dance moves in fights. She's also really kind and likes to help people. Don't think she's not tough, though!

When the Rangers met RJ, they didn't realise this laid-back guy was their master, but he quickly proved himself when he saved them in a fight. He broke the news that they were Power Rangers, gave them their Solar Morpher glasses and got them training with their new weapons. Lily uses a Jungle Bo, Theo has Jungle Tonfa batons and Casey fights with the Jungle Chucks.

Meanwhile, Dai Shi is living up in his Lair. It's a really creepy place - an island in the sky, surrounded by mountains. From there, he plots to rid the world of humans and have an army of animal spirits take over!

TOP SECRET

Dai Shi's loyal second-in-command is Camille, a terrifying creature who can camouflage herself into any background. She has a tongue like a lizard, which she uses to attack, and some pretty nasty battle armour.

Camille also has - and this is the really disgusting bit - a fly called Flit who lives in her stomach. The poor thing is an ancient warrior who she turned into a fly. These days Flit just buzzes around spying on people for Camille.

With such fearsome enemies, it's a good job the Rangers have so many tricks up their sleeves. For starters, they can power up to Beast Spirit forms for extra fighting power. Casey has the Tiger Beast Spirit, Theo the Jaguar and Lily has the Cheetah. These Spirits can combine to form the Jungle Pride Megazord, which has awesome power and some cool moves like the Savage Spin and Super Kick.

And there's another Ranger too - Dominic, the White Rhino Ranger. He saved me from a falling sign using his special Rhino powers to drill a hole right through it . . . phew . . . breathe . . .

The Rangers have Jungle Master Modes and a whole lot of gear - like Casey's Strike Rider Cruise motorbike and weapons like the Claw Cannon, the Jungle Mace and the Jungle Fan.

TOP SECRET

13

Dai Shi has a fight on his hands, that's for sure, but he does have help. He and Camille have lessons from the Sky Overlord Carnisoar, a nasty hawk-like creature and the Sea Overlord Jellica, who is a jellyfish spirit master.

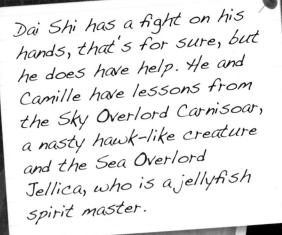

TOP SECRET

Dai Shi also has an an army of Rinshi warriors and some nasty characters like the Five Fingers of Poison - they have really icky names like Rantipede and Stingerella.

Meanwhile, the Rangers are building up some awesome skills and learning to work better as a team. To help them they have the Spirit Masters. One of Theo's masters is Master Swoop, who taught him to concentrate better and gave him some Bat powers and the Jungle Fan weapon. Lily's first master was Master Phant. At first he refused to teach her to use the Elephant Mace weapon, but then she refused to move from his house until he did!

Casey gets lessons from Master Rilla, who has the spirit of a gorilla. He taught Casey to overcome his worst childhood fear (monsters hiding in his closet!).

All the Rangers can call on their new animal powers to make the Jungle Pride Megazord more powerful.

So, it looks to be an interesting job for me here at Jungle Karma Pizza. With all this going on, no two days are ever the same. One thing is for sure – since I met the Power Rangers, life is certainly not boring any more!

Fran.

POWER RANGERS JUNGLE FURY PROFILE

RED

Casey, the Red Ranger, has less experience than the Blue and Yellow Rangers, but he has proved himself to be a worthy leader of the Jungle Fury team.

RED RANGER'S TIGER BEAST SPIRIT

FULL NAME:
Casey Rhodes

BRAINS 9

TOP GEAR:
Solar Morpher, Strike Rider

SPEED 8

ZORDS:
Tiger, Shark, Gorilla

POWER 8

TOP SKILLS:
Kung Fu, fixing things

ABILITY 8

RANGER

HOBBIES:

Making pizzas

COOLNESS — 9

WEAPONS:

Jungle Chucks, Battle Claws, Claw Booster

SKILL — 8

How many Jungle Chucks can you see around the page?

Answer on page 68.

17

PIZZA PUZZLE

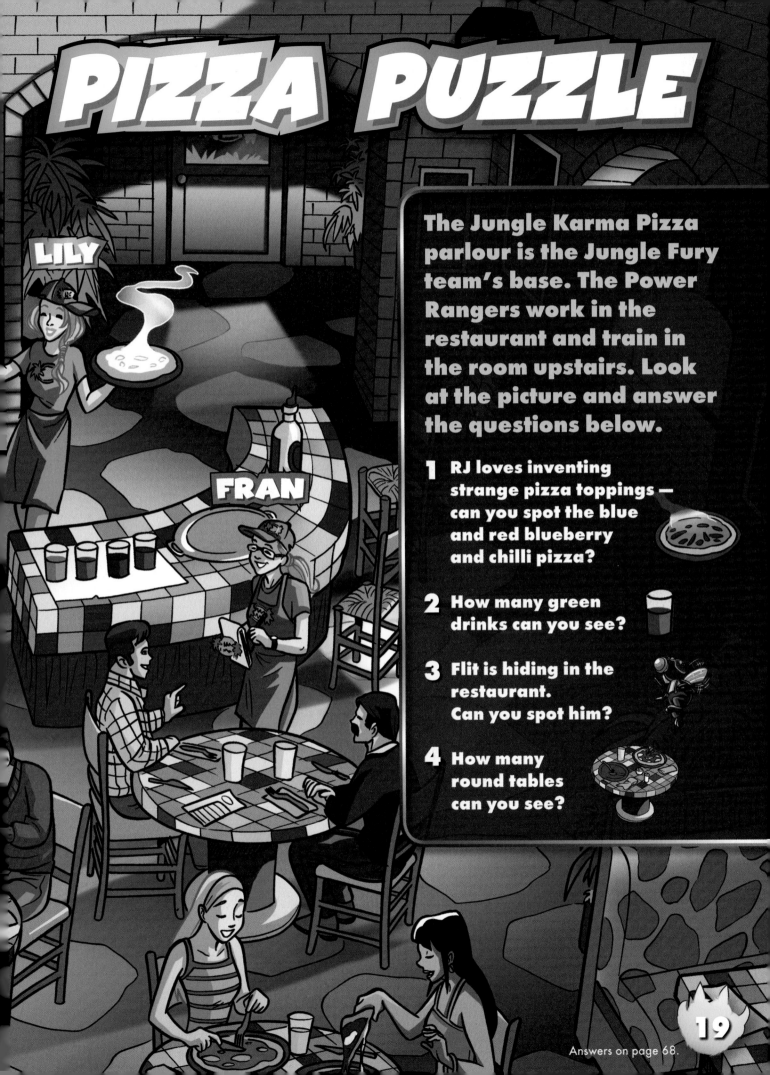

LILY

FRAN

The Jungle Karma Pizza parlour is the Jungle Fury team's base. The Power Rangers work in the restaurant and train in the room upstairs. Look at the picture and answer the questions below.

1 RJ loves inventing strange pizza toppings — can you spot the blue and red blueberry and chilli pizza?

2 How many green drinks can you see?

3 Flit is hiding in the restaurant. Can you spot him?

4 How many round tables can you see?

Answers on page 68.

PROFILE

With his masterful fighting skills, Theo, the Blue Ranger is a star player on the Jungle Fury team. He takes his role very seriously, striving to be the best in the fight against the evil Dai Shi.

FULL NAME:

Theo Martin

| BRAINS | 9 |

TOP GEAR:

Solar Morpher

| POWER | 7 |

ZORDS:

Jaguar, Bat, Antelope

| SPEED | 8 |

BLUE RANGER

TOP SKILL:

Fighting with his Jungle Tonfa weapons

ABILITY	10

HOBBIES:

Having lunch with Lily, the Yellow Ranger

COOLNESS	8

WEAPONS:

Jungle Tonfa, Battle Claws, Jungle Fan

SKILL	10

TOP FACT!

At the elite Pai Zhuq martial arts academy, Theo was one of the guardians over the evil spirit, Dai Shi.

JUNGLE WORDS

Can you find these Jungle Fury words in the wordsearch? The words can be read up, down, forwards or backwards. Tick the box next to each word as you find it.

M	Z	X	M	O	R	P	H	E	R
G	F	H	K	Q	X	I	H	S	Q
J	U	N	G	L	E	Z	K	L	C
F	R	R	Q	X	Z	Z	J	K	A
D	Y	I	M	B	E	A	S	T	M
H	Q	N	H	K	Q	Z	X	T	I
T	J	S	X	Q	Z	P	P	N	L
G	Q	H	H	X	Z	Z	H	G	L
F	L	I	T	L	X	G	V	E	E
Q	V	X	Z	L	P	P	P	F	Z	X

 PIZZA

 RINSHI

 CAMILLE

 FLIT

 BEAST

 MORPHER

 JUNGLE

 FURY

CAMILLE AND FLIT

These pictures of Camille and Flit look the same, but 6 things are different in picture 2. Colour in a paw print each time you spot a difference.

1

2

Answers on page 68.

Artwork – concept: Gianluca Barone; pencil: Luca Usai; ink: Oscar Scalco; colour: Dario Calabria.

FEEDING FRENZY

The **Power Rangers Jungle Fury** team arrive at Ocean Bluff where the evil spirit **Dai Shi** has sent **Rinshi** warriors to test them. The Rangers quickly morph and summon their personal weapons . . .

Jungle Chucks!

Jungle Tonfa!

Jungle Bo!

Soon . . .

That hit the spot! I – oh no!

Nice meal, Rangers? It was **your last!** Rinshi – power up!

The Rinshi Beast transforms into an ugly, terrifying locust monster . . .

Ha ha! Dai Shi will grow stronger with these people's fear!

Ranger time! Let's **morph!**

But as they are about to begin, Camille's tongue suddenly flicks out . . .

SLURRK!

No! My sunglasses! **I can't morph!**

27

Flit, keep away – oh, come here!

I'll take those!

Jungle Beast! Spirit Unleashed!

The Rangers quickly move to the next level, releasing their Animal Spirits . . .

Red Tiger!

Blue Jaguar!

Yellow Cheetah!

Their Animal Spirit forms slash through the locust's tough shell . . .

RRRAAWWR!

SHWUNNK!

RRRRAAWWWRR!

Outnumbered by the powerful Rangers, Camille flees . . .

Curse them! Today they've won - tomorrow will be different!

The victorious Rangers power down . . .

Two battles won! We are **cookin'**!

Yes, and we weren't sluggish – even after eating . . .

Maybe there's a lesson . . . look at Camille and Flit – shows you shouldn't fight on an empty stomach!

The End

JUNGLE BADDIES

1 Starting at number 1, join the dots to reveal Dai Shi's true form. Now give him some colour.

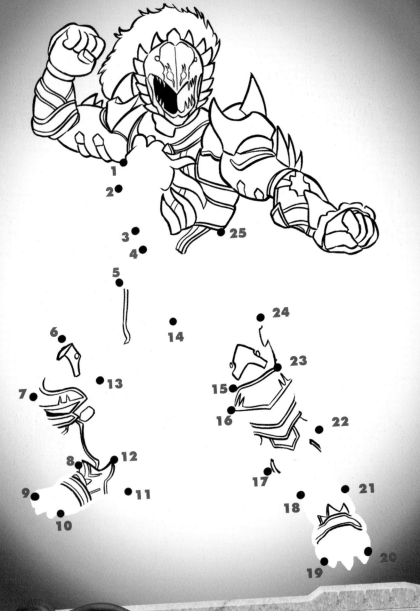

2 Put these Rinshi into size order from biggest to smallest. Write numbers from 1-4 in the circles with 1 for biggest. The first one is done for you.

a

b

1 d

c

POWER RANGERS JUNGLE FURY

PROFILE

VIOLET

RJ, the Violet Wolf Ranger, is the Jungle Fury Rangers' laid-back teacher. Though his lessons seem strange, he teaches the Rangers all they need to fight their enemies.

FULL NAME:
Robert James

BRAINS	9

TOP GEAR:
Wolf Morpher

SPEED	9

ZORDS:
Wolf, Tiger, Jaguar

POWER	9

WOLF RANGER

POWERS:
RJ is a master of Pai Zhuq martial arts

GOODNESS   9

HOBBIES:
Meditating, inventing new pizzas

COOLNESS   10

WEAPONS:
RJ's favourite weapons are his fists, knees and feet

SKILL   10

RJ

TOP FACT!
RJ's father is Master Finn, a Pai Zhuq master with the spirit of the shark.

POWER RANGERS JUNGLE FURY GAME

The Blue Ranger is fighting evil Dai Shi. Write your own scores for each character in the paw prints, then add them up to see who wins.

SCARINESS /10

SIZE /10

GOODNESS /10

CLOTHES /10

The Blue Ranger usually fights with Jungle Tonfa weapons. How many can you see hidden on these pages?

TOTAL

BLUE RANGER

BATTLE ZONE

SCARINESS /10

SIZE /10

GOODNESS /10

CLOTHES /10

TOTAL

DAI SHI

37

Answer on page 68.

Artwork – concept: Gianluca Barone; pencil: Luca Usai; ink: Oscar Scalco; colour: Dario Calabria.

POWER RANGERS JUNGLE FURY

PACK ATTACK

An evil spirit, **Dai Shi**, has taken over the body of Jarrod, once a student at the **Pai Zhuq martial arts academy** with the Power Rangers Jungle Fury team. In his forbidding lair, Dai Shi plots to make his terrible plans come true . . .

Ha ha! I will rid the Earth of humans and have animals take over!

He has an army of Rinshi warriors to help him . . .

Hyena pack Rinshi – your time has come . . .

The more human fear there is, the greater my powers grow. So Rinshi – spread your terror!

Release your Beast Spirits!

LOST RANGER

Can you show the Yellow Ranger the quickest way out of Dai Shi's Lair?

START

FINISH

Answer on page 68.

COLOUR CAMILLE

This is Camille in her battle armour. Draw over the lines to finish the picture, then colour it in as neatly as you can.

CAMILLE

PROFILE

With her cheetah-like speed, Lily, the Yellow Ranger, is a mean opponent. She was a cheerleader in high school and now uses her dance moves in fights!

FULL NAME:

Lily Chilman

BRAINS	8

TOP GEAR:

Solar Morpher, Claw Boosters

SPEED	10

ZORDS:

Cheetah, Elephant, Penguin

POWER	7

YELLOW RANGER

POWERS:
Super speed

| GOODNESS | 8 |

HOBBIES:
Dancing

| COOLNESS | 8 |

WEAPONS:
Jungle Bo, Jungle Mace

| SKILL | 9 |

How many pictures of the Yellow Ranger's Beast Spirit can you see hidden on these pages?

LILY

Answer on page 68.

JUNGLE

The Rangers are the masters of some pretty awesome weapons. Find out about them with these puzzles.

1 The Yellow Ranger defends herself with her Jungle Bo weapon. How many of them can you see in this pile?

WEAPONS

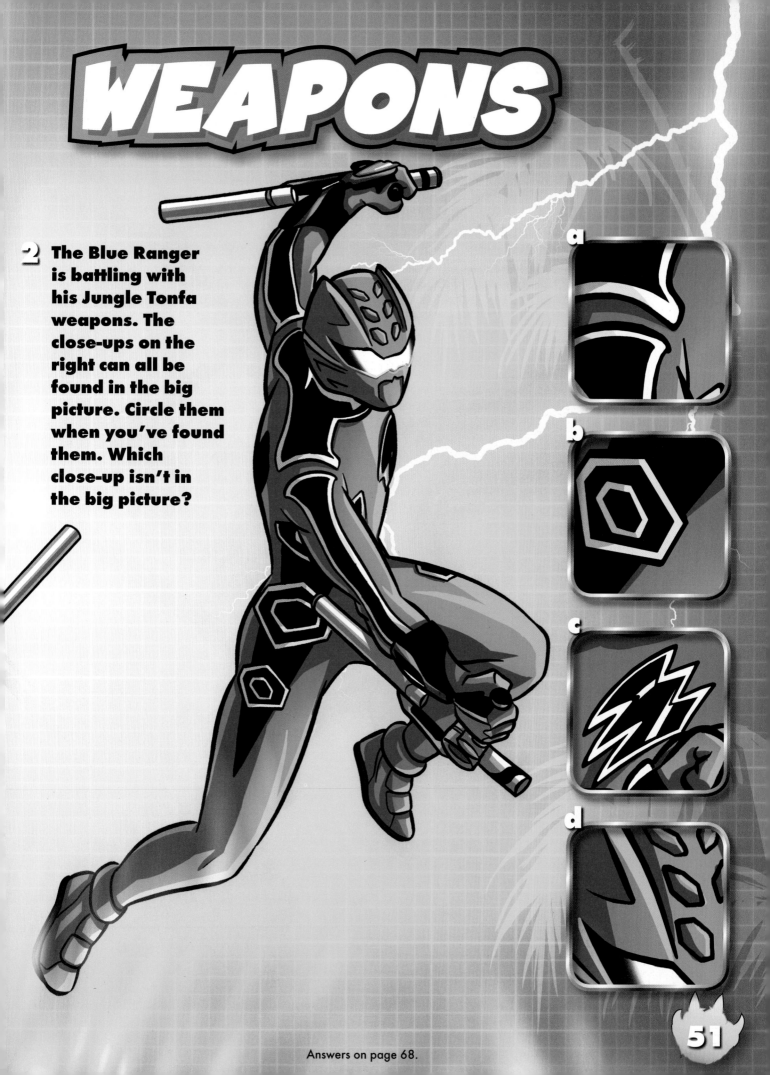

2 The Blue Ranger is battling with his Jungle Tonfa weapons. The close-ups on the right can all be found in the big picture. Circle them when you've found them. Which close-up isn't in the big picture?

a

b

c

d

51

Answers on page 68.

Artwork – concept: Gianluca Barone; pencil: Luca Usai; ink: Oscar Scalco; colour: Dario Calabria.

POWER RANGERS JUNGLE FURY

THE ENEMY WITHIN

In a desert area just outside Ocean Bluff, the **Power Rangers** have formed the **Jungle Pride Megazord**. They are practising with its weapon - the **Setsukon** . . .

Huhh-ya-tahh!

I'm normally more careful than that. Ah, well – just a little scratch . . .

How wrong you are! Hidden against the cactus, I pressed a **poisoned thorn** deep into your arm!

Yet as they left, Camille – working for Dai Shi and able to camouflage herself - steps away from the cactus . . .

Nearing the Jungle Karma Pizza parlour . . .

So RJ, not straight back to work, is it? RJ?

Raaahh!

What in the world?

54

Faced by a crazed RJ, far superior in fighting skills, the trio morph . . .

Jungle Beast! Spirit Unleashed!

The Rangers have their work cut out – their own trainer is suddenly bad guy **numero uno**!

They've gone for their weapons!

Yet they're not attacking, just setting up a strong defence!

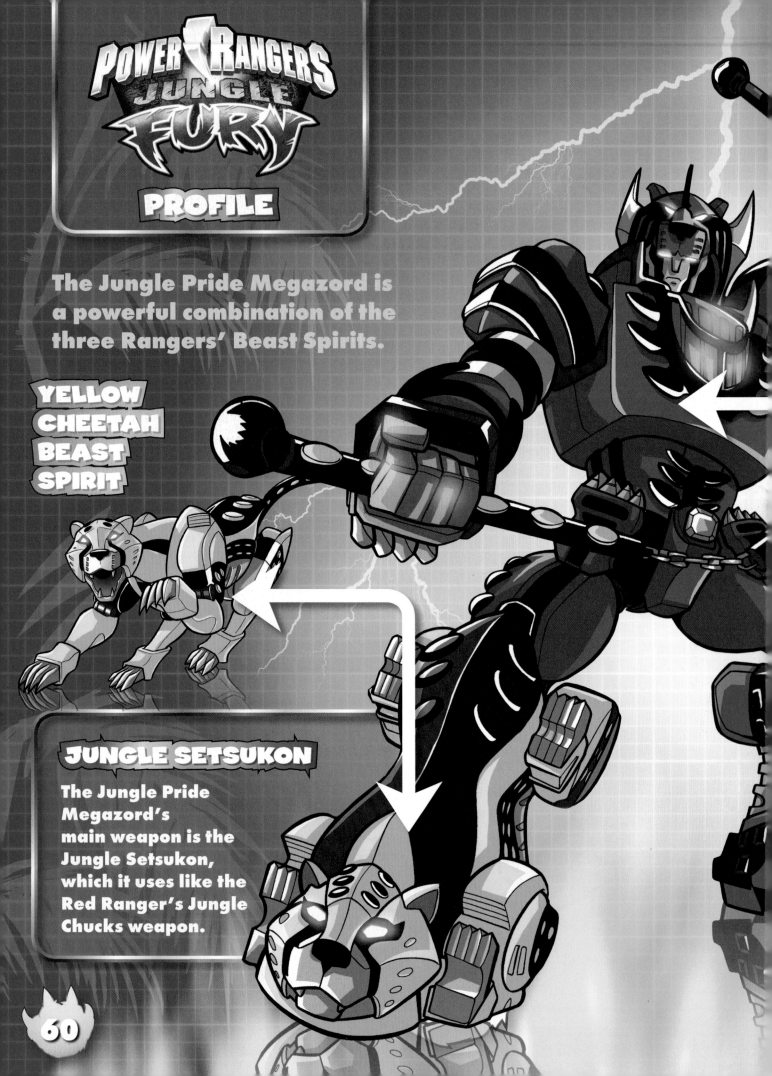

POWER RANGERS JUNGLE FURY

PROFILE

The Jungle Pride Megazord is a powerful combination of the three Rangers' Beast Spirits.

YELLOW CHEETAH BEAST SPIRIT

JUNGLE SETSUKON

The Jungle Pride Megazord's main weapon is the Jungle Setsukon, which it uses like the Red Ranger's Jungle Chucks weapon.

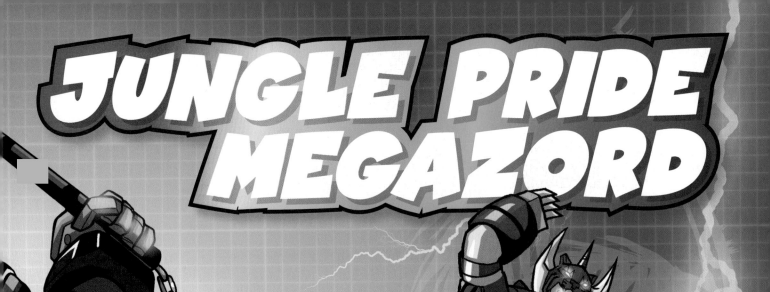

JUNGLE PRIDE MEGAZORD

RED TIGER BEAST SPIRIT

The Jungle Pride Megazord can perform some mighty moves and he packs a punch with his Super Kick!

BLUE JAGUAR BEAST SPIRIT

PROFILE

WHITE

Dominic, the White Rhino Ranger, is a late but fearsome addition to the Jungle Fury team. He has one of the toughest animal spirits — the Rhino.

FRAN

FULL NAME:
Dominic Hargan

| BRAINS | 8 |

TOP GEAR:
Power Bracelet

| SPEED | 8 |

ZORDS:
Rhino Steel Zord

| POWER | 7 |

RHINO RANGER

POWERS:
Cutting through hard substances, such as metal

GOODNESS (9)

HOBBIES:
Travelling the world, reading, talking to Fran

COOLNESS (8)

WEAPONS:
Jungle Bo, Jungle Mace

SKILL (9)

Dominic once used his Rhino power to save Fran from a falling sign!

DAI SHI'S LAIR

The evil Dai Shi is in his lair with Camille by his side. Look at the picture and answer the questions.

1 How many Rinshi can you see in the picture?

2 Can you spot Flit the fly?

3 Who is Dai Shi's loyal second-in-command?

Answers on page 68.

HOW TO DRAW

Copy the picture of the Red Ranger's Solar Morpher by tracing over the blue lines in the box below.

RED SOLAR MORPHER

JUNGLE

Think you know all there is to know about the world of Jungle Fury? Try this quiz to find out! Tick the paw print next to your answer.

1 What is the name of the Rangers' teacher?

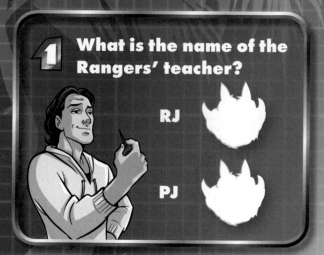

RJ

PJ

2 What is the name of the place where the Jungle Fury team meets?

The Jungle Karma Pizza parlour

The Jungle Karma Bowling Hall

3 Which Ranger owns the Jungle Chucks weapon?

4 Which evil spirit is the Jungle Fury team's worst enemy?

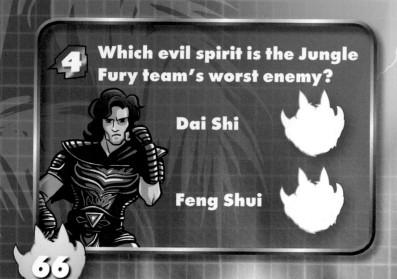

Dai Shi

Feng Shui

5 Which weapon is the Jungle Tonfa?

66

CHALLENGE

6 Which of these Animal Beast Spirit Zords is called the Red Tiger Beast Spirit?

7 Which of these baddies is called a Rinshi?

8 What is the name of the warrior Camille holds captive in insect form?

Blip

Flit

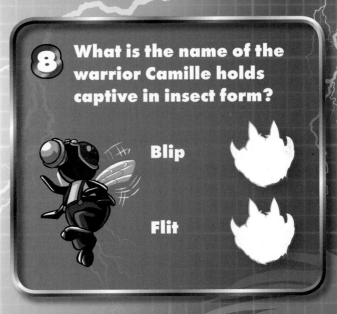

9 Which of these pictures is the Jungle Pride Megazord?

10 Which picture is a Solar Morpher?

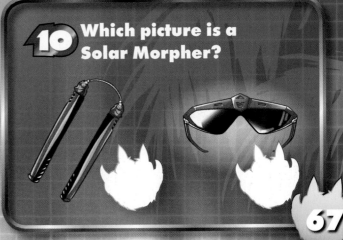

67

ANSWERS

PAGE 17
RED RANGER

7 Jungle Chuck weapons.

PAGE 19
PIZZA PUZZLE

1) The blue and red blueberry and chilli pizza is in Casey's hand; 2) 2 green drinks; 3) Flit is hiding on the shelves by the left-hand wall; 4) 4 round tables.

PAGE 22
JUNGLE WORDS

M	Z	X								
G		H	K	Q	X		H	S	Q	
							K	L		
F			Q	X	Z		J	K		
D			M				J			
H	Q		H	K	Q	Z	X	T		
T	J		X	Q	Z	P	P	N	G	
T	G	Q		H	X	Z	Z	H	G	
				L	X	G	V	E		
Q	V	X	Z	L	P	P	F	Z	X	

PAGE 23
CAMILLE AND FLIT

PAGE 33
JUNGLE BADDIES

2) 1 - d, 2 - a, 3 - c, 4 - b.

PAGE 36
BATTLE ZONE

6 Jungle Tonfa weapons.

PAGE 46
LOST RANGER

PAGE 48
YELLOW RANGER

5 Yellow Beast Spirits.

PAGE 50
JUNGLE WEAPONS

1) 5 Jungle Bo weapons; 2) C isn't in the picture.

PAGE 64
DAI SHI'S LAIR

1) 2 Rinshi; 2) Flit is next to the Rinshi on the right; 3) Camille.

PAGE 66
JUNGLE CHALLENGE

1) RJ; 2) the Jungle Karma Pizza parlour; 3) the Red Ranger; 4) Dai Shi; 5) the short weapon; 6) the red tiger; 7) the warrior wearing a blindfold; 8) Flit; 9) the red, yellow and blue creature; 10) the red sunglasses.

HAVE YOU SEEN POWER RANGERS MAGAZINE?

FREE RANGER PHONE!

100% OFFICIAL

POWER RANGERS JUNGLE FURY

ACTION-PACKED COMIC STRIP!

PLUS

POWER RANGERS OPERATION OVERDRIVE

PUZZLES
POSTERS
ACTIVITIES

AS SEEN ON TV!

This gift complies with the European Toy Safety Standard EN71. Warning! Not suitable for children under 3 years due to small parts. Supplied by HMA Creative, Bucks, HP19 8DZ. Please retain this information for future reference.

CE 0-3

Issue60 EGMONT

FUELLED WITH POWERED-UP RANGER FUN!

 STORIES

 PUZZLES

 POSTERS

 GAMES

FREE GIFT WITH EVERY ISSUE!

Available from all good newsagents and supermarkets

OUT EVERY 3 WEEKS!